CW00343181

Sheik, Rattle and
The Wise Men's Nativity

by Sheila Wilson
edited by Alison Hedger

Duration approx. 30 minutes
Key Stages 2 + Lower 3

Dedicated to my Godson, Sebastian John Nye, with love.

This Nativity best suits children aged 8 to 12 years, but can be enjoyed
by a wider age range. There are opportunities for children as young
as 5 years to take part and enjoy the music.

(Sheik/Sheikh: wise man or elder)

The music is in a variety of styles and includes
a lullaby, 'rock and roll', ballad and blues.

SONGS

1. There's No Room!	*Innkeepers + All*
2. Let There Be Peace On Earth	*Boys, Girls (two parts)*
3. Sheik and Rattle and Roll!	*All*
4. Sleep, Little One	*Mary, Angels + All*
5. Following Your Star	*All (two parts)*
6. We Bring Gold	*Wise Men + All*
7. I'd Rather Follow You	*Solo Sheik + Wise Men Trio + All*
Finale: Medley of Songs 2, 6, 5, and 3	

The Pupil's Word Booklet is available separately and contains the drama and song words
Order No. GA11017

A matching tape cassette of the music for rehearsals and performances is available,
Order No. GA11018, side A with vocals included and side B with vocals omitted.

© Copyright 1996 Golden Apple Productions
A division of Chester Music Limited
14/15 Berners Street, London W1T 3LJ, England.

Order No. GA11858

ISBN 978-1-84772-221-8

AUTHOR'S NOTE

When I found out that 'Sheik' could mean 'wise man', the ideas for this musical fell into place. I was interested in portraying the Nativity from the Wise Men's perspective. The staff, children and parents at St. Peter's School, Marlow, threw themselves into the premiere of SHEIK, RATTLE AND ROLL! in December 1995 with their customary enthusiasm and style. I'm very grateful to them all!

EDITOR'S NOTES ON THE NAMES OF THE THREE WISE MEN

The usual collective name for the Wise Men is the Magi. This is the Latin plural of the word Magus, which literally means Wise Man.

The Magi followed the miraculous guiding star to Bethlehem where they paid homage to the infant Jesus as King of the Jews. (Matthew 2 v. 1–12). Eastern tradition sets the number of Magi at twelve, but Western tradition preferred three, basing this on the three gifts.

The Biblical story was embellished and by the third century the Magi were considered to be kings. This can be linked to the prophecy in Psalm 72 v.11 'Yea, all kings shall fall down before him:'. By the eighth century the three members of the Magi were credited with names: MELICHIOR, GATHASPA and BITHISAREA; these are now commonly known as MELCHIOR, GASPAR or CASPAR and BALTHAZAR. Tradition has it that Melchior (meaning king of light) was from Persia and brought gold, the emblem of royalty; Caspar (meaning the white one) was from India and brought frankincense for divinity; and Balthazar (meaning the lord of treasures) was from Arabia and brought myrrh, to depict the prophetic persecution until death.

We shall never know for certain what the true names of the Wise Men were, but in this musical Sheila Wilson has used artistic licence and called them SHEIK, RATTLE and ROLL!

1.
THERE'S NO ROOM!

Innkeepers + All

way! Can't you see we're so bu - sy here____ to -

- day? There's no room! No room for you to

hire! So please don't en - quire!

No - one here can pro - vide what you_____ de - sire.

All: What are they_____ to do? Lord, give them

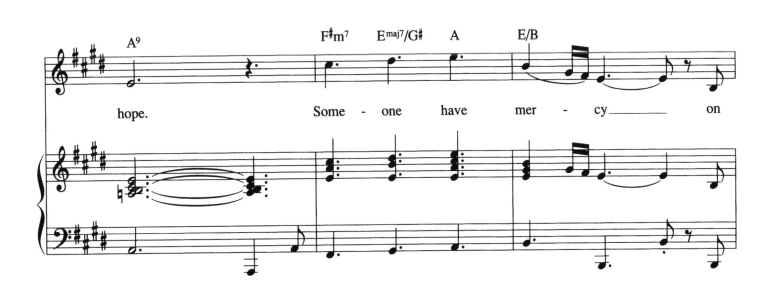

hope. Some - one have mer - cy_____ on

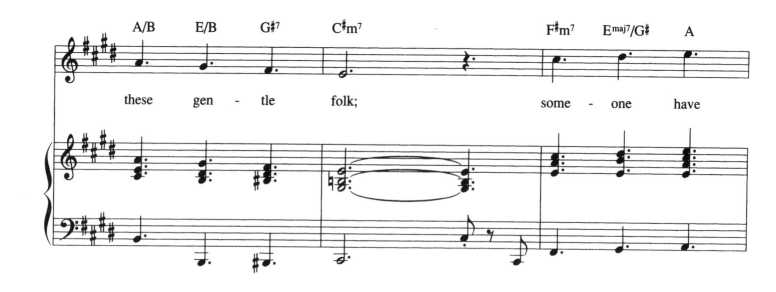

these gen - tle folk; some - one have

mer - cy___ on these gen - tle folk.

All: There's

2.
LET THERE BE PEACE ON EARTH

Boys + Girls (two parts)

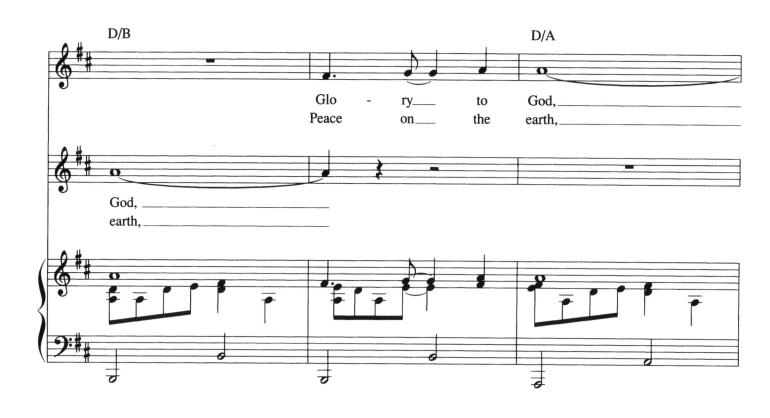

song continues overleaf

The optional ending for use as indicated on page 11 of the script.

9

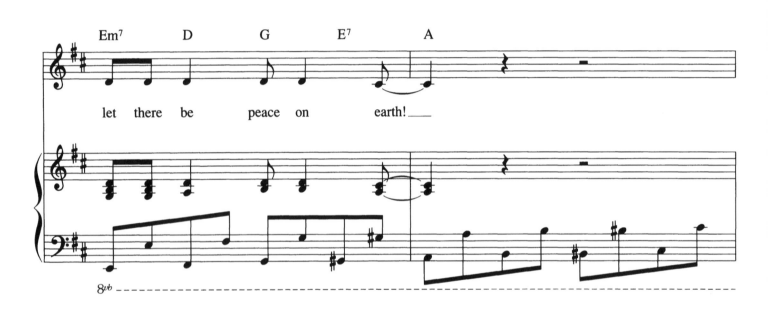

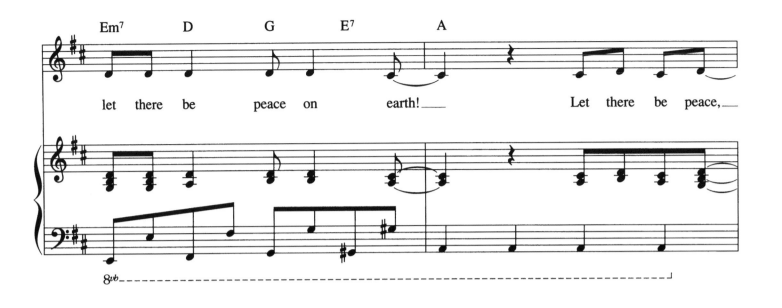

let there be peace on earth! ___ Let there be peace, ___

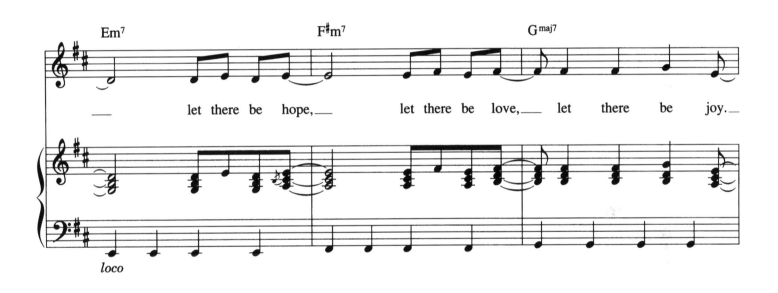

___ let there be hope, ___ let there be love, ___ let there be joy. ___

___ Let there be peace, ___ let there be hope, ___ for ev - ery girl ___

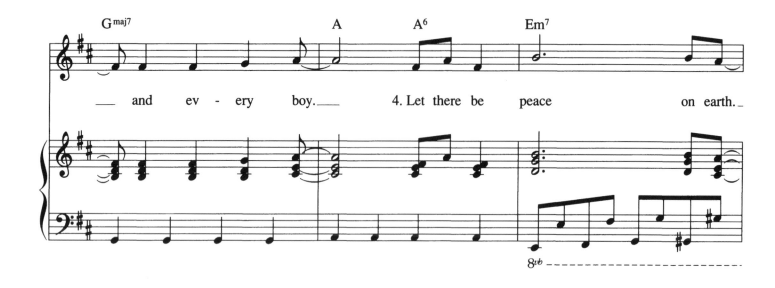

_ and ev - ery boy.__ 4. Let there be peace on earth._

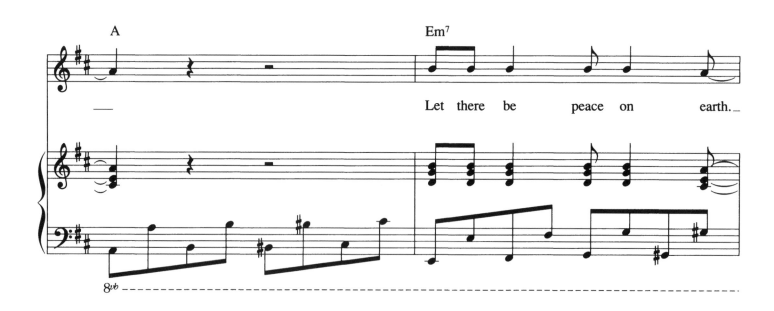

_ Let there be peace on earth._

_ Let there be peace on earth.

Let there be peace on earth.___ 5. Let there be peace,___

___ let there be hope,___ let there be love,___

___ let there be joy.___ Let there be peace,___ let there be hope,___

Sing this section three times, first _ff_ second _f_ third _mp_, ending in a whisper.

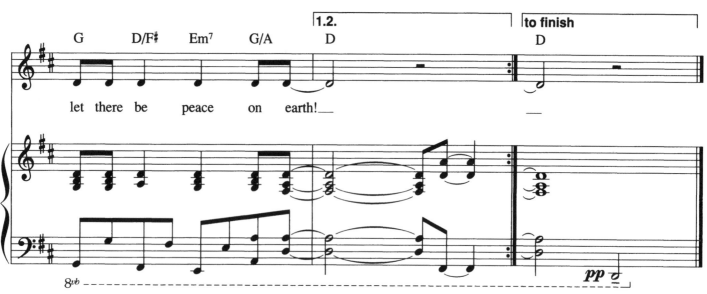

3.
SHEIK AND RATTLE AND ROLL!

All

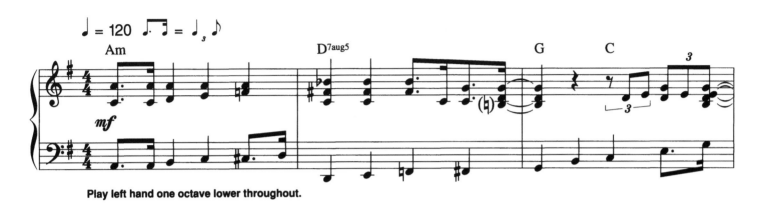

Play left hand one octave lower throughout.

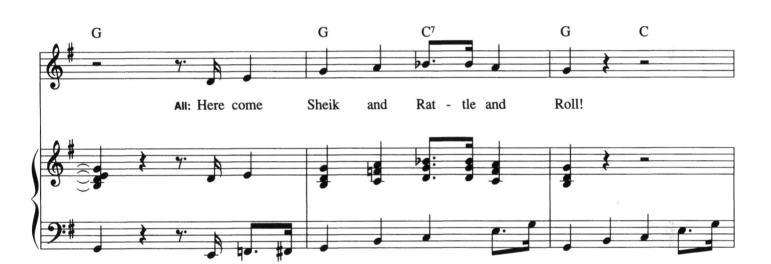

All: Here come Sheik and Rat - tle and Roll!

Sheik and Rat - tle and Roll! Sheik and Rat - tle and

star that points due west,___ then in the morn - ing,___
mean - ing of their quest.___ Then in the morn - ing,

as day is dawn - ing,___ some - times Wise Men don't
you'll see them yawn - ing.___ Ev - en Wise Men should

ev - en stop to rest! ___
get them - selves some rest! ___

CODA

Sheik and Rat - tle and Roll! ___

rall. e cresc.

tremolo

ff

4.

SLEEP, LITTLE ONE

Mary + Angels + All

(Angels/All) guard your life; ___ all men___ shall

see your light; ___ but oh, what___ a

sac - ri - fice.___ So sleep, lit - tle one,___

go to sleep.

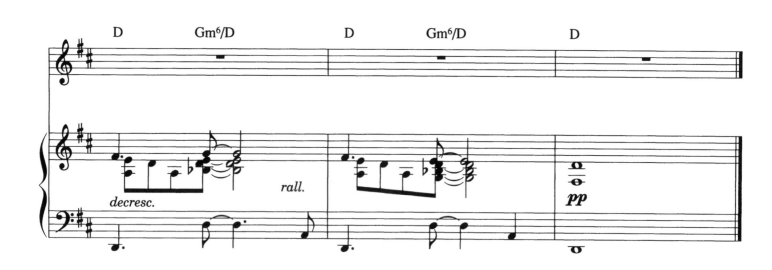

5.
FOLLOWING YOUR STAR

All (two-parts)

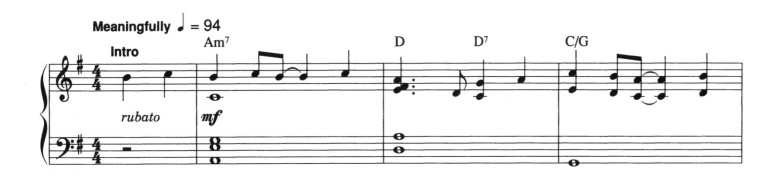

All: Lord, I'm fol - low - ing___ Your star; how I

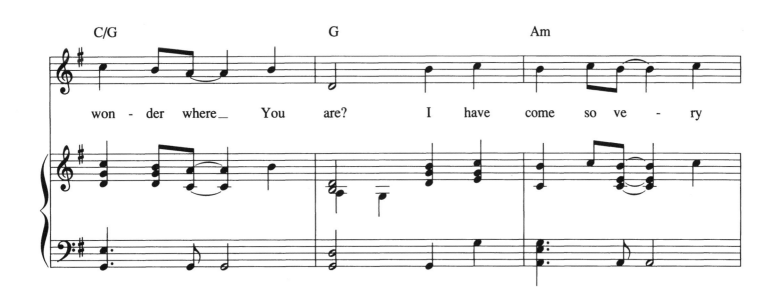

won - der where___ You are? I have come so ve - ry

far, and I'm still fol-low-ing___ Your star. Lord, I'm

fol-low-ing___ Your star; how I won-der where___ You

are? I have come so ve - ry far, and I'm still

fol-low-ing___ Your star.

Piano solo

6.

WE BRING GOLD

Wise Men + All

gold,   we bring myrrh, ___   we bring frank - in - cense to You. ___

___ And we bring hearts that are full ___ of sweet

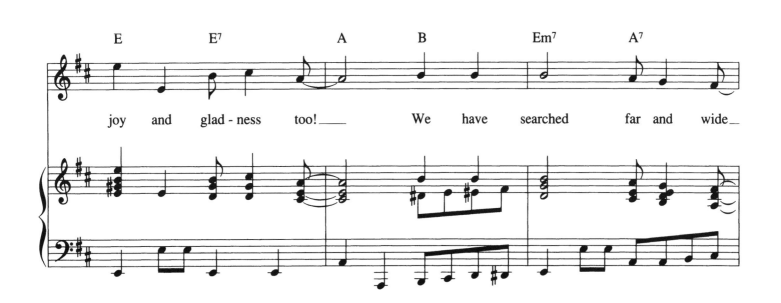

joy and glad - ness too! ___ We have searched far and wide ___

with Your star as our guide;___ now we

kneel by Your side___ and wor - ship You.

You.

7.

I'D RATHER FOLLOW YOU

Solo Sheik + Wise Men Trio + All

Thoughtfully, then purposefully ♩ = 100

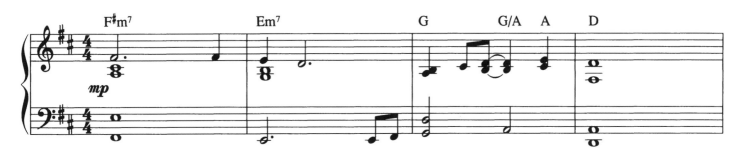

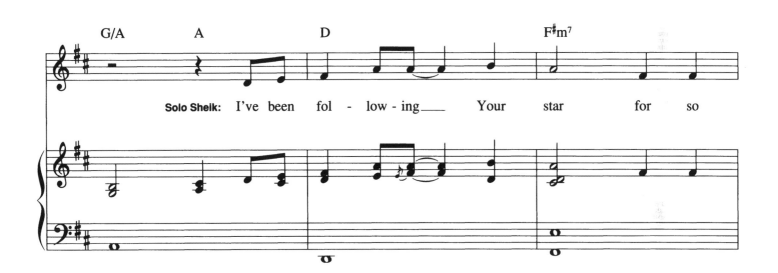

Solo Sheik: I've been fol - low - ing___ Your star for so

long,___ and now it's gone,___ I

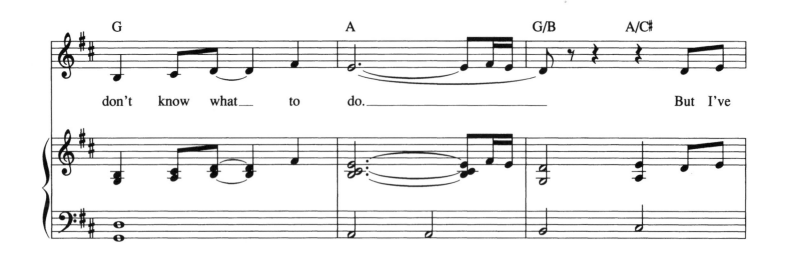

don't know what___ to do._____ But I've

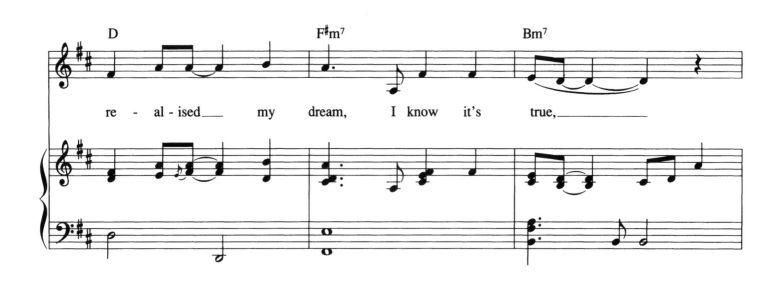

re - al - ised___ my dream, I know it's true,_____

from now on___ I'd ra - ther fol - low You.

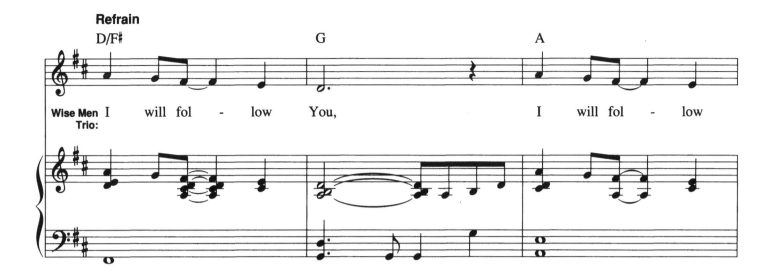

Refrain

Wise Men Trio: I will fol - low You, I will fol - low

You. Mmm, Lord Je - sus, I will fol - low

You. All: I've been fol - low - ing__ Your star for so

35

long,_____ and now it's gone,_____ I

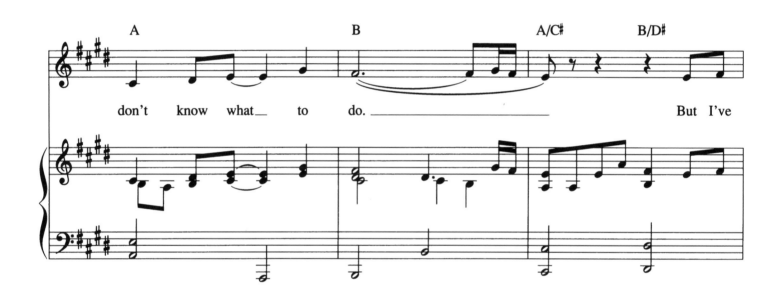

don't know what_ to do._____ But I've

re - al - ised_ my dream, I know it's true,_____ But I've

from now on___ I'd ra - ther fol - low You.

Refrain

I will fol - low You, I will fol - low

You. Mmm, Lord Je - sus, I will fol - low

You.   I'm

⊕ CODA

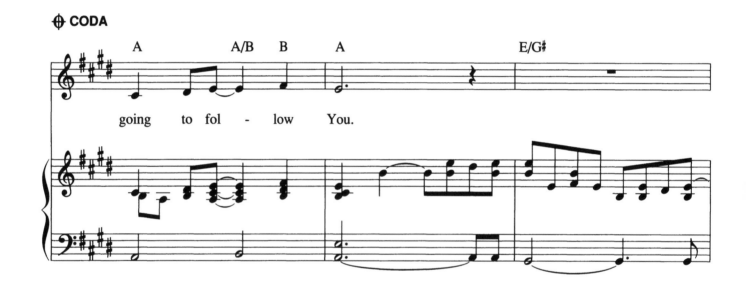

going   to fol - low   You.

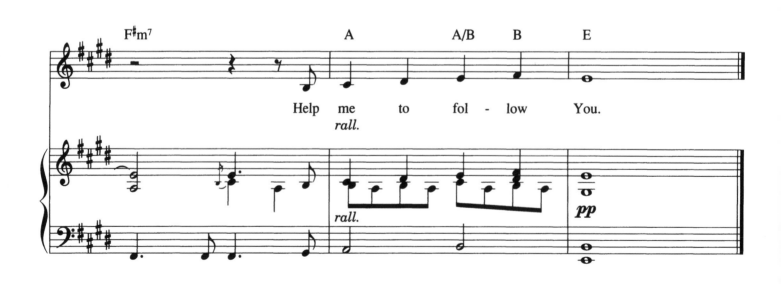

Help   me   to   fol - low   You.

rall.

MEDLEY of Songs 2, 6, 5 and 3

All

Let there be peace,___ let there be hope,___ let there be love,___

___ let there be joy.___ Let there be peace,___ let there be hope,___

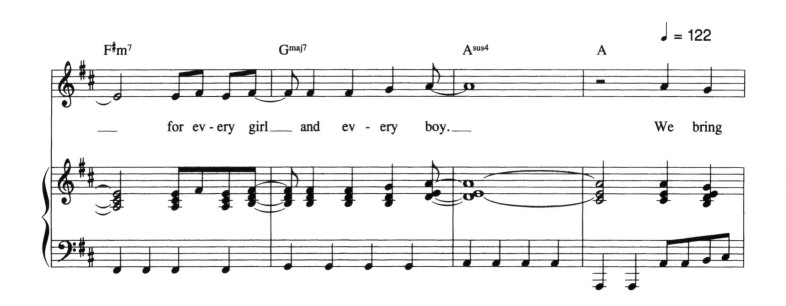

___ for ev-ery girl___ and ev-ery boy.___ We bring

gold, we bring myrrh, __ we bring frank - in - cense to You. __

__ And we bring hearts that are full __ of sweet

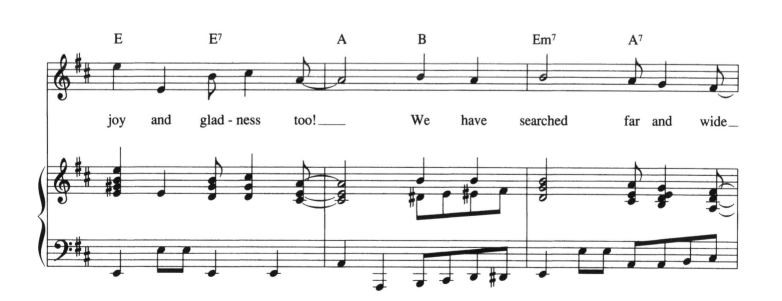

joy and glad - ness too! __ We have searched far and wide __

with Your star as our guide;____ now we

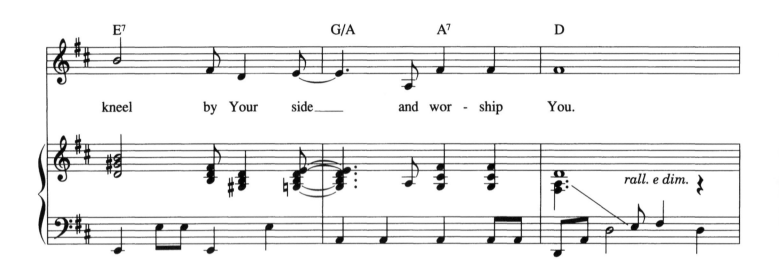

kneel by Your side____ and wor - ship You.

I've been fol - low - ing____ Your star for so long,____

44

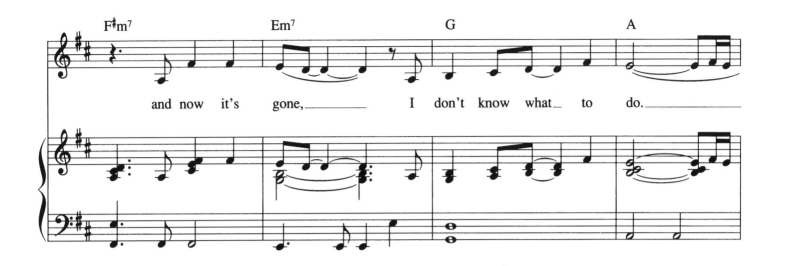

and now it's gone,_____ I don't know what_ to do._____

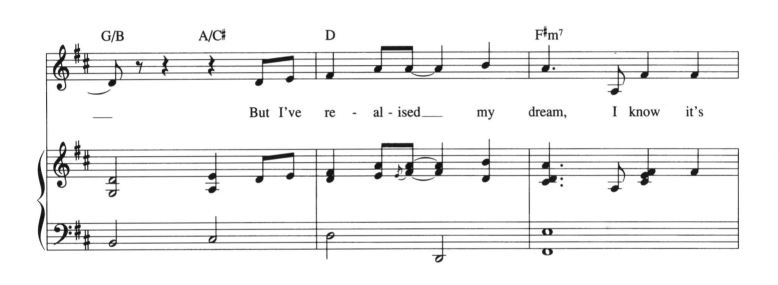

But I've re - al - ised_ my dream, I know it's

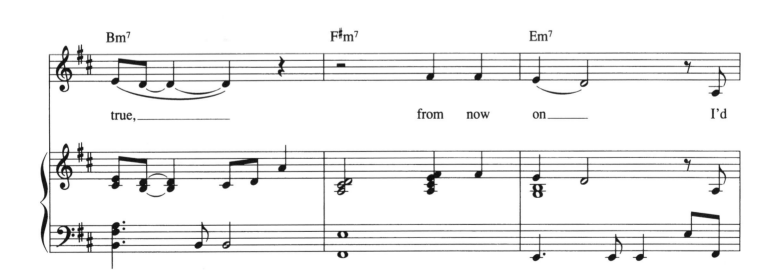

true,_____ from now on_____ I'd

ra - ther fol - low You. I will fol - low You,

I will fol - low You. Mmm, Lord Je - sus,

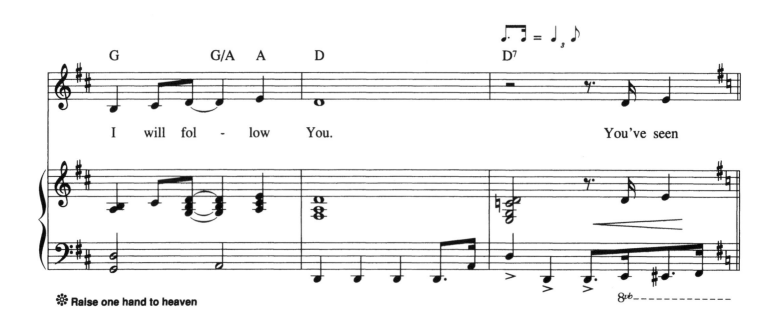

I will fol - low You. You've seen

see script page 15 for hand-jives

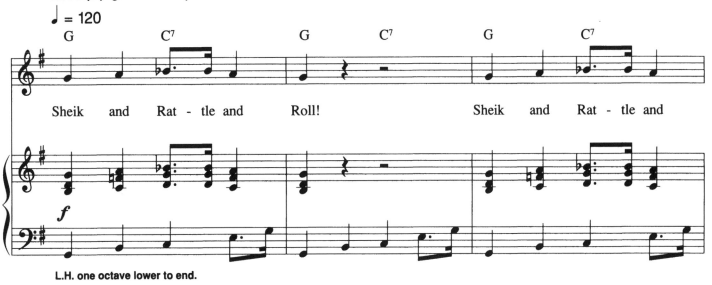

Sheik and Rat - tle and Roll! Sheik and Rat - tle and

L.H. one octave lower to end.

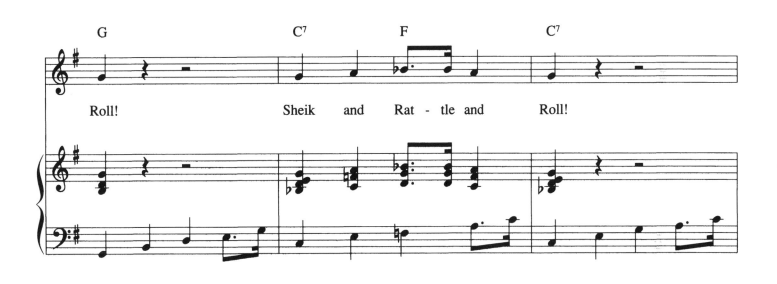

Roll! Sheik and Rat - tle and Roll!

Sheik and Rat - tle and Roll! Thank you for join - ing

in our Christ - mas thank _ you for join - ing in our Christ - mas thank _

_ you for join - ing in our Christ - mas Show! _

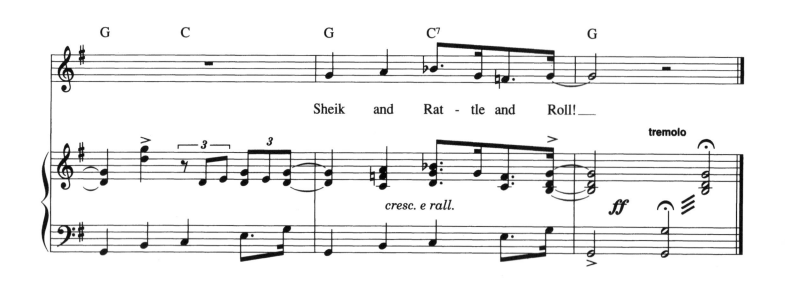

Sheik and Rat - tle and Roll! _

cresc. e rall. ff tremolo

Printed and bound in Great Britain by
Caligraving Limited Thetford Norfolk